Usborne

First Sticker Book
Diggers

Illustrated by Dan Crisp

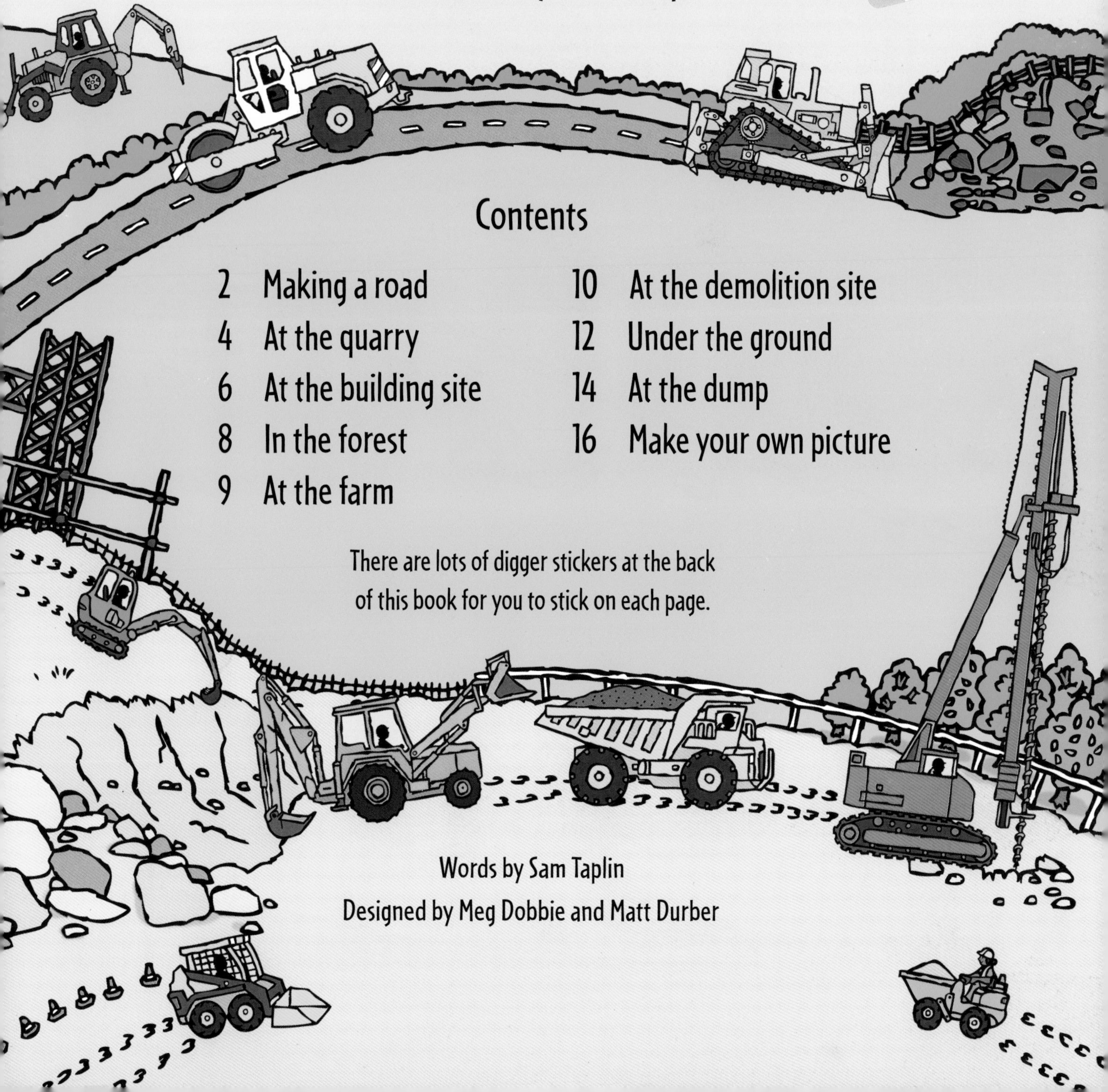

Contents

There are lots of digger stickers at the back of this book for you to stick on each page.

Words by Sam Taplin

Designed by Meg Dobbie and Matt Durber

Making a road

There are lots of busy diggers working here.
Excavators and front loaders are digging up a road,
while road graders and pavers are making a new one.

ROAD CLOSED
ROAD CLOSED

At the quarry

Front loaders and excavators are scooping up heavy rocks and carrying them away from the quarry.

At the building site

Bulldozers are flattening the ground at the building site, and excavators are digging holes where the buildings will go.

In the forest

Log loaders and claw diggers are carrying away trees that have been chopped down in the forest.

At the farm

Front loaders and hedge trimmers are working on the farm.

At the demolition site

Huge diggers called long reach excavators are smashing the old buildings at the demolition site.

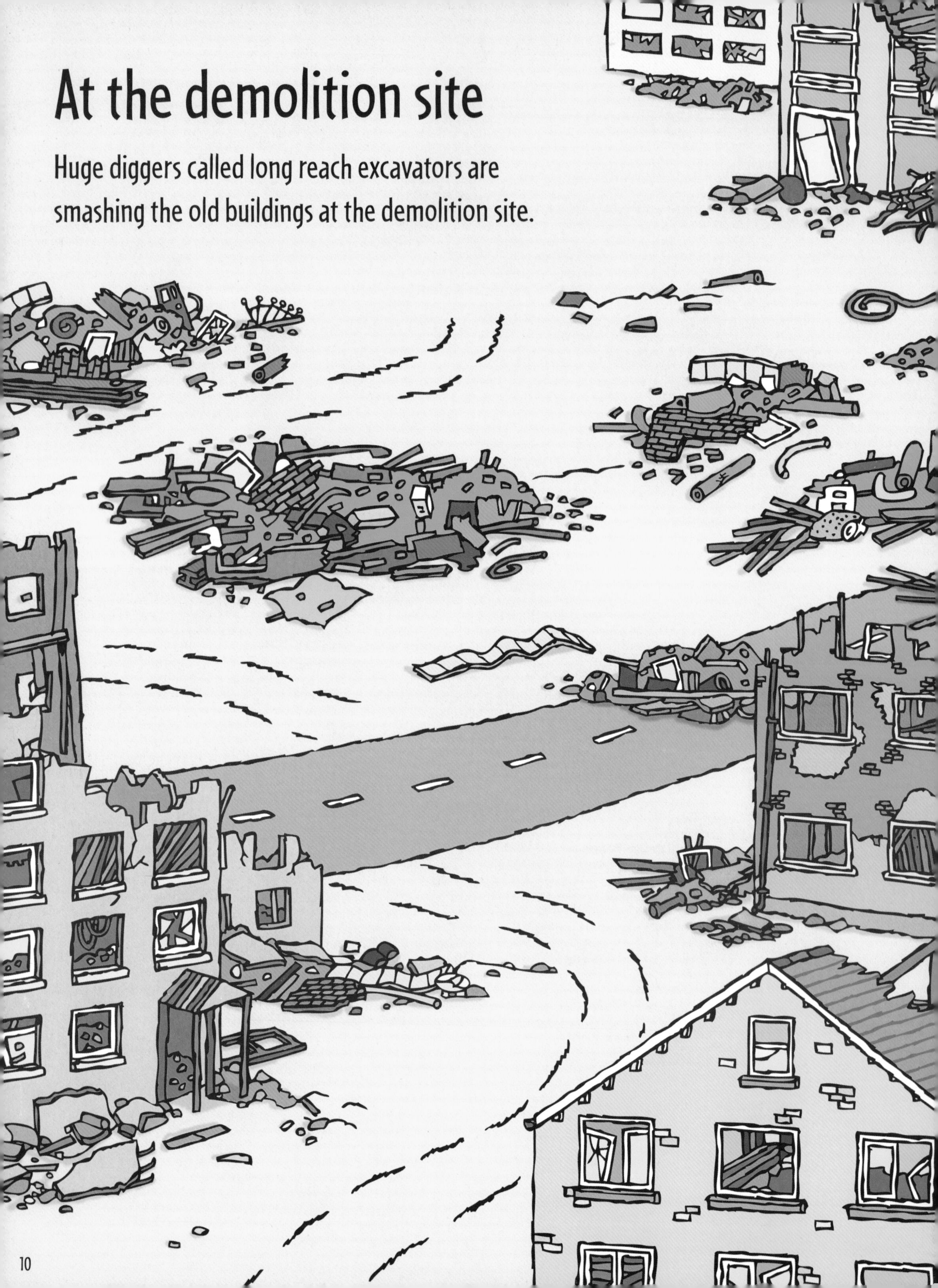

Under the ground

Roadheaders with spiky blades are cutting tunnels deep under the ground. Big drilling machines are making holes in the surface.

At the dump

Scrap-handlers are crushing old cars at the dump, and bulldozers are sorting the other waste into different heaps.

Make your own picture

Use the stickers to make your own picture on this page.

Making a road

Backhoe loader with hammer

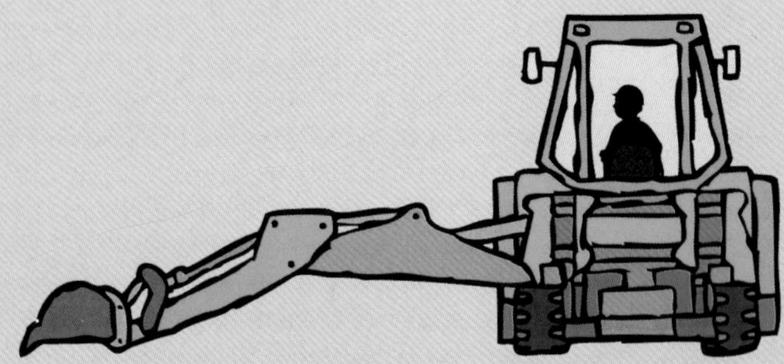

Backhoe excavator

Skip

Dump truck

Flatbed truck

Mini dump truck

Road grader

Paver

Loader excavator

Mini excavator

Road roller

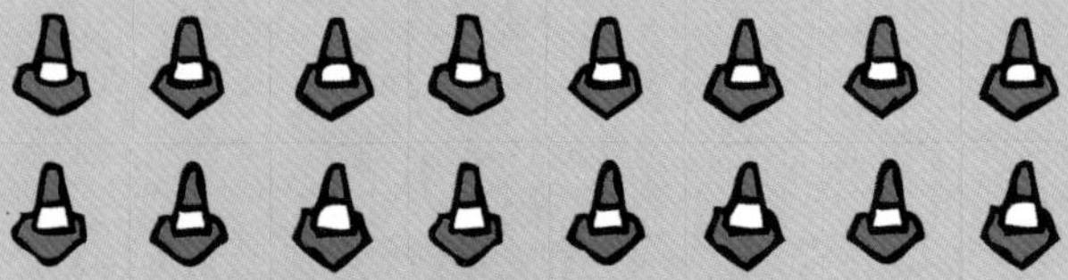

Traffic cones

Front loader

At the quarry

Front loader

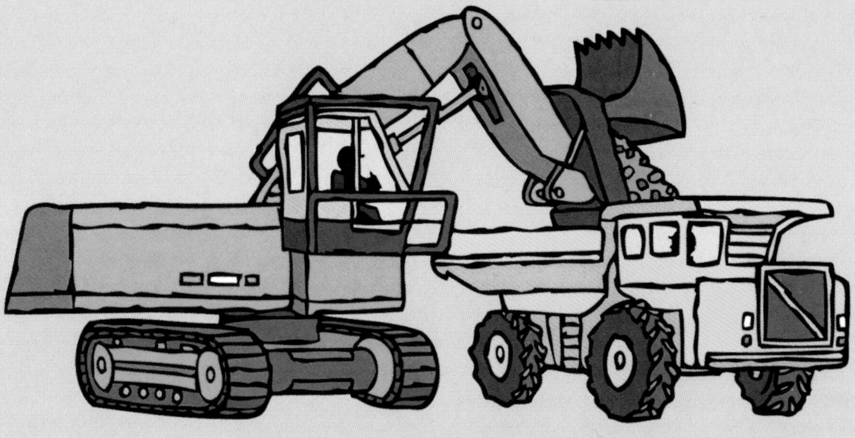

Face-shovel loading dump truck

Double-wheeled front loader

Front loader with backhoe

Excavator breaking rocks

Rotating face-shovel

Bulldozer

Rock breaker

At the building site

Front loader

Concrete mixer truck with pump

Mini dump truck

Excavator with lifting forks

Tracked excavator

Mini dump truck

Heavy load dump truck

Rock breaker

Builder with wheelbarrow

Builder with cement mixer

Skid steer

Bulldozer

In the forest

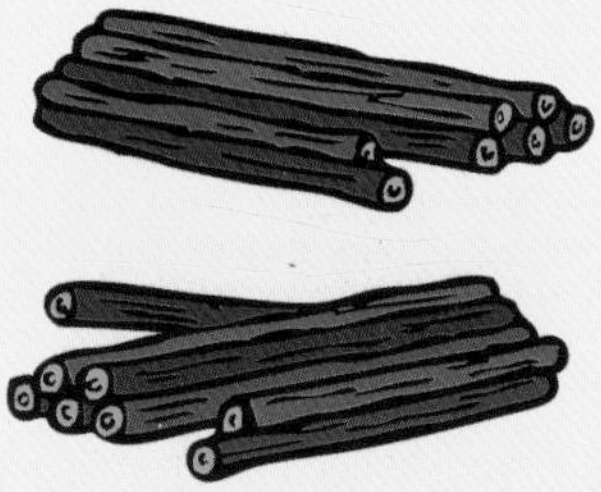

Timber

Claw digger

Log trailer

Front loader

Skidder with grapple

Log loader

At the farm

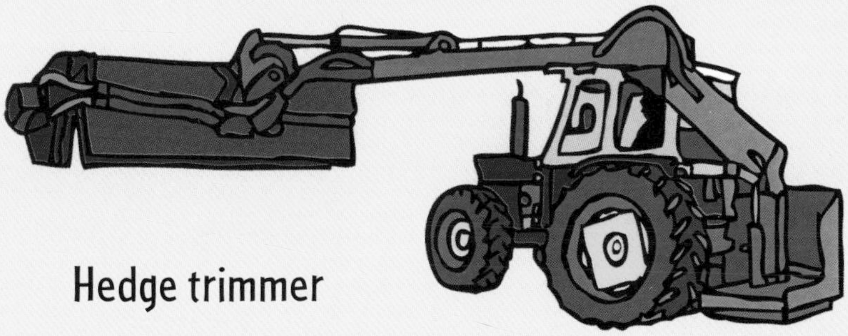

Hedge trimmer

Front loader with bale-fork

Tractor with backhoe

Front loader moving muck

At the demolition site

Skid steer

Excavator with hammer

Tracked bulldozer

Skip

Excavator

Mini dump truck

Mini dump truck

Long reach excavator

Dump truck

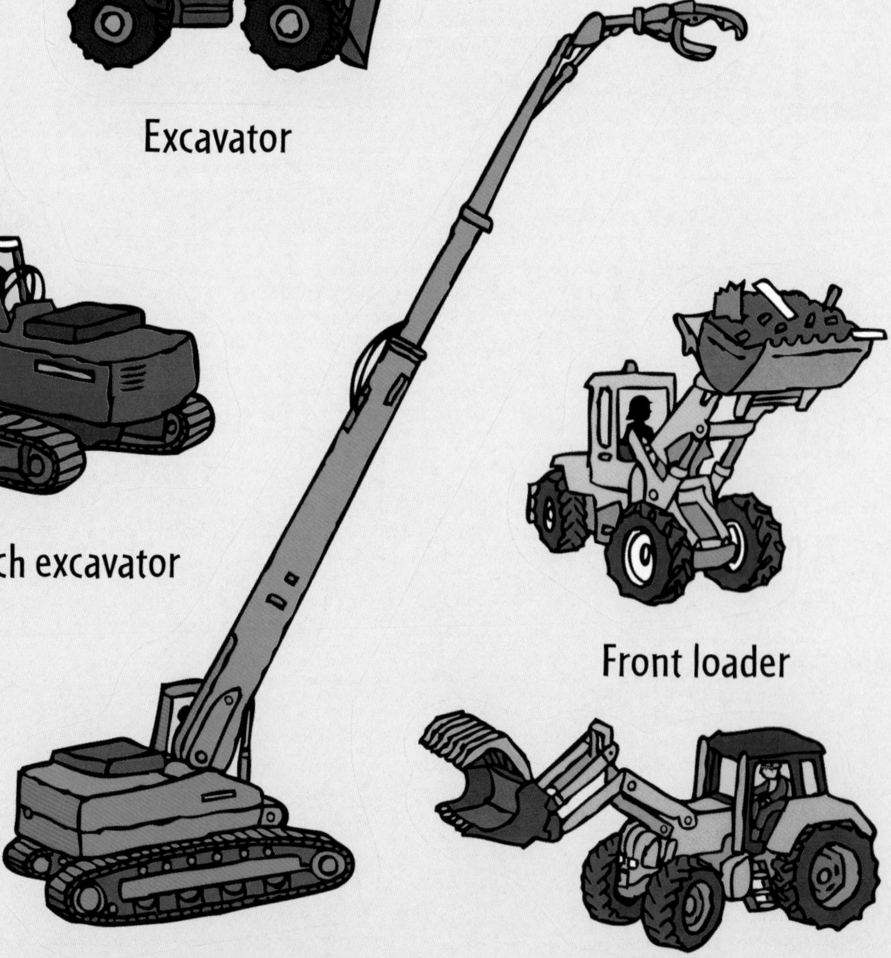
Front loader

Long reach excavator

Front loader with claw

Under the ground

Loader excavator

Roadheader

Heavy load dump truck

Front loader with claw

Mini dump truck

Mini dump truck

Skid steer

Excavator

Skid steer

Mini excavator

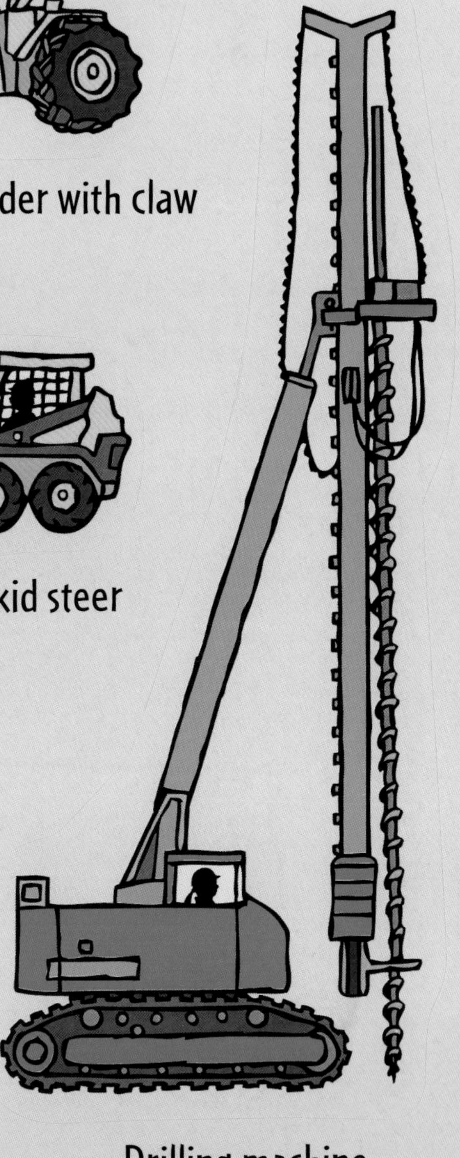

Drilling machine

At the dump

Giant bulldozer

Skid steer

Scrap-handler

Bulldozer moving waste

Tracked bulldozer

Excavator

Backhoe loader

Mini dump truck

Truck delivering soil

Excavator

Make your own picture

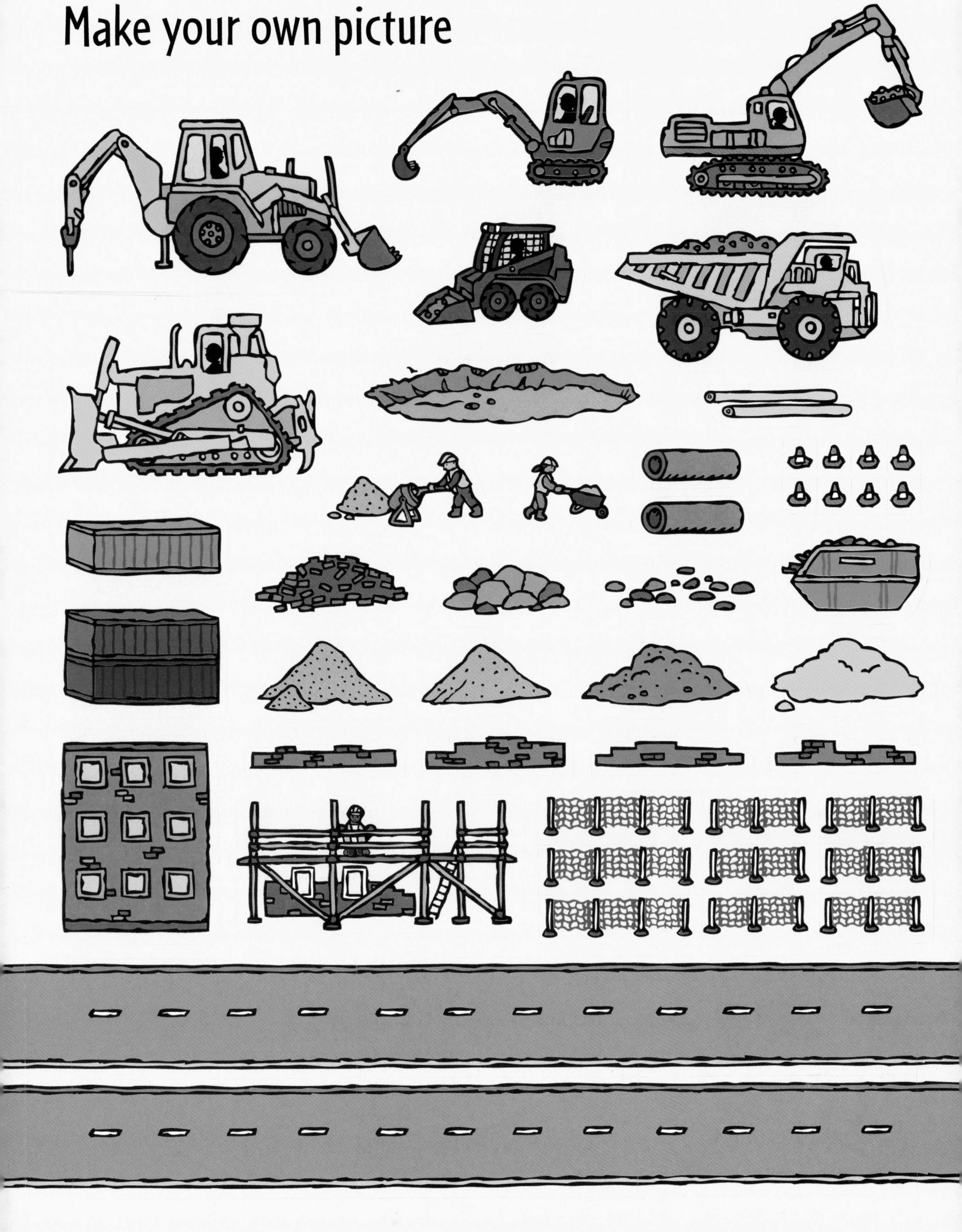